HELP WITH HOMEWORK
SCIENCE
ESSENTIALS

HI, MY NAME IS **KITCAT**...

... AND I'M **DIG**

WE ARE HERE TO HELP YOU THROUGH THESE EXERCISES. START AT THE BEGINNING AND DON'T DO TOO MUCH IN ONE GO.

IT WON'T BE EASY ALL THE TIME. SOME PAGES CAN BE TRICKY, BUT WE'VE GIVEN YOU THE ANSWERS AT THE BACK IN CASE YOU GET REALLY STUCK. NO PEEPING, THOUGH! YOU WILL RECOGNISE A LOT OF THIS FROM THE WORK YOU DO AT SCHOOL. NOW DON'T YOU WISH YOU'D PAID MORE ATTENTION?! GOOD LUCK!

D0532968

Autumn
Publishing

Is it alive?

You can test whether something is alive or not. All living things answer 'yes' to these seven tests (or processes) of life.

1. Does it move?
Plants turn their leaves to the Sun. Animals move about from place to place.

2. Does it reproduce?
Plants develop seeds from which new plants grow. Animals produce offspring.

3. Is it sensitive?
Plants and animals are sensitive to changing conditions in their environment and adapt to change.

4. Does it feed?
All living things need food to provide energy. Only plants can produce their own food from sunlight.

5. Does it produce waste?
Plants and animals produce waste that they need to expel.

6. Does it respire?
All living things take in oxygen. Oxygen is needed to release energy from food.

7. Does it grow?
Babies become children, then adults. Plants grow from seedlings to become bigger plants.

Draw lines from the labels (below left) to the things listed opposite.

ALIVE

WAS ONCE ALIVE

NEVER ALIVE

acorn seedling

fallen autumn leaf

plank of wood

pebble

brick

hopping rabbit

2

Plant parts

The different parts of a plant are used in the seven life processes (see opposite).

Write the missing words in the sentences below to describe the function of the different parts of a flowering plant. Choose from these words:

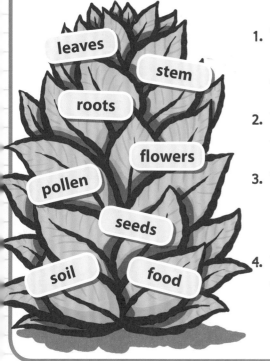

leaves
stem
roots
flowers
pollen
seeds
soil
food

1. The flowers attract insect pollinators. The male parts of the flower produce _pollen_. When the flowers die, fruits and _seeds_ are formed.

2. The _leaves_ use sunlight to turn carbon dioxide and water into _soil_ – a process called photosynthesis.

3. The _stem_ carries nutrients and water from the roots to the leaves and _flowers_. It also holds the plant upright so that it can grow towards the Sun.

4. The _____ hold the plant in the ground and soak up water and nutrients from the _____.

Here is a cross-sectional view of a flower. Label it using the words below.

petal
sepal
stigma *(female)*
ovary
seeds
stamen *(male)*
pollen
pollinator

1 _____
2 _____
3 _____
4 _____
5 _____
6 _____
7 _____
8 _____

Stick a reward sticker here!

3

Fruits and seeds

In order to protect their seeds, some plants produce fruits. Avocados and plums, for example, contain a single large seed. By contrast, melons and tomatoes have many tiny seeds.

Look inside some of the fruits you eat. Draw seeds in the fruits pictured below.

orange

apple

pea pod

strawberry

cucumber

tomato

melon

pomegranate

grape

Order the main stages in the plant life cycle. Write the numbers 2 to 4 in the boxes in the correct order to describe the life of a plant. The first stage has been identified for you.

Seeds are scattered by the wind and animals. ☐

Plants are pollinated by insects and the wind. ☐

Seeds germinate and new plants start to grow. 1

Fertilised plants make fruits and seeds. ☐

Stick a reward sticker here!

4

Seed dispersal

Plants disperse their seeds in various ways.

1. Some seeds are dispersed in animal droppings, e.g. mice eat blackberries and then plant the seeds wherever they leave their droppings!

2. Sticky burrs are carried away in animals' fur.

3. Sycamore or ash seeds grow 'wings' and float on the wind.

4. Dandelion seeds parachute through the air.

5. Poppies shake their seeds in the wind.

Match the five descriptions of seed dispersal (above) to the pictures below. Write the matching number next to each picture.

Get it?

'Disperse' is a scientific word meaning 'scatter'.

Stick a reward sticker here!

5

Food chains

Plants and animals depend on each other for survival. For example:

- Some plants need animals for fertilisation. Insects spread pollen from one plant to another. Some plants depend on animals to disperse these seeds.

- Animals need plants for food and shelter. Birds eat berries and fruits. They use twigs to build their nests in the spring.

Food chains describe who eats whom. A food chain always starts with a plant. Study the food chains below.

PLANT → INSECT → MOUSE → OWL

ALGAE → SHRIMP → FISH → SEAL → POLAR BEAR

Write the names of these animals in the correct place in the food chains below.

FROG   SLUG   RABBIT

Get it?

Plants are called 'producers' because they can make (produce) their own food. Animals are 'consumers' because they eat (consume) plants or other animals.

GRASS → _____ → THRUSH

GRASS → _____ → FOX

GRASS → INSECT → _____ → HAWK

6

Habitats

Habitats are the places where plants and animals live. Plants and animals are adapted to their habitats in special ways. For example, the colour and pattern of the hawk moth's wings match the bark of the trees found in its habitat.

Write a few words to describe how the following animals are adapted to their habitat.

Crocodile – _____

Owl – _____

Tiger – _____

Which of the adaptations match these animals?

Draw a line to join each one.

How does each animal use their adaptation?

long, sharply-pointed beak	hedgehog
large, trumpet-shaped ears	seal
sharp spines on body	anteater
skin that matches its surroundings	heron
thick layer of body fat	impala
long snout and tongue	leaf frog

_____

_____

_____

_____

_____

_____

7

Using keys

A 'classification key' uses a series of questions to identify a group of plants or animals.

Look at the pictures below and answer the questions to identify each animal. Write the name of each animal within the key.

housefly   spider   millipede   snail   slug

Does it have legs?

Yes   No

Does it have 6 legs?   **Does it have a shell?**

Yes   No   Yes   No
------------   ------------   ------------

Does it have 8 legs?

Yes   No

Does it have more than 20 legs?

Yes

Complete the table using these words: crocodile, mammal, fish, duck, amphibian.

Definition	Belongs to the group called:	Example
Breeds in water but spends time on land	_____	FROG
Cold blooded, breathes air and has scales	REPTILE	_____
Cold blooded, has scales and gills, lives in water	_____	SALMON
Warm blooded, young feed on milk	_____	APE
Has feathers and wings	BIRD	_____

8

Life cycles

A 'life cycle' is the way something changes from young to adult. Some animals have babies that look like mini-adults, but others undergo amazing changes (called metamorphosis) during their life cycle.

Order these animal life cycles in the correct stages from youngest to adult:

FROG   FROGSPAWN   FROGLET   TADPOLE

1. _____   2. _____   3. _____   4. _____

CATERPILLAR   EGG   BUTTERFLY   PUPA

1. _____   2. _____   3. _____   4. _____

EGG   ANT   COCOON   LARVA

1. _____   2. _____   3. _____   4. _____

Now order these words in the correct stages in the human life cycle:

BABY   EGG   TEENAGER   CHILD   ADULT

1. _____   2. _____   3. _____   4. _____   5. _____

On each line below, draw the three stages in the life cycle of a housefly:

EGG   MAGGOT   ADULT

1. _____   2. _____   3. _____

Write down one difference between the life cycle of a human and the life cycle of a housefly:

_____

_____

Human body

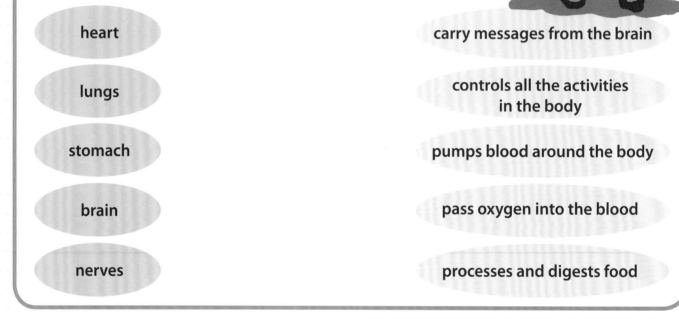

Your body is like an amazing machine with many different parts (called 'organs') used for different things.

What do these different parts of the body do? Join the name of each part to the special job it does.

heart   carry messages from the brain

lungs   controls all the activities in the body

stomach   pumps blood around the body

brain   pass oxygen into the blood

nerves   processes and digests food

Healthy heart

Your heart never stops working, even when you are asleep. When you are active, it has to work even harder but that's not a bad thing because exercise is good for your heart.

Which things are bad for your heart? Look at the list of words in the box to the right and circle the things that are bad for your heart.

fatty foods	lack of exercise
vegetables	alcohol
running	fruit
tobacco	drugs
exercise	lots of salt

TEST IT OUT!

Your pulse is a measure of how fast your heart is beating. Measure your pulse using a watch or timer. Count the beats per minute to find your pulse rate.

At rest: _____ *beats per minute*

After five minutes exercise: _____ *beats per minute*

What do you notice? Now find out how long it takes for your pulse to go back to its resting rate. The quicker it goes back the fitter you are!

Stick a reward sticker here!

Write the missing words in the spaces below. Choose from the following:

BLOOD   LUNGS   BODY   OXYGEN   HEART   CARBON DIOXIDE

Your _____ works like a pump. It has two sides so that blood can go in two directions: one artery pumps _____ to the lungs and the other artery pumps blood to the rest of the body.

Your blood contains _____ and food which your body needs. When you exercise, your _____ uses more oxygen so your heart beats faster to increase the supply.

Your lungs are like sponges filled with tiny pockets of air. When you breathe in you are filling your _____ with oxygen and when you breathe out you are breathing out _____.

Here are some more major parts of the body.
Join the name of each part to the special job it does.

liver

kidneys

bladder

skeleton

blood vessels

protects your organs and helps you to move

carry food and oxygen to the body cells

filter waste from your blood and make urine

cleans your blood and stores vitamins

stores urine

Stick a reward sticker here!

11

Diet and health

A healthy body needs a variety of food for energy, growth and repair.

There are four main food groups.

Group:	Good for:	For example:
CARBOHYDRATES	ENERGY	PASTA, BREAD, POTATOES
PROTEINS	GROWTH AND REPAIR	FISH, MEAT, EGGS
FATS	ENERGY AND WARMTH	BUTTER, CHEESE
VITAMINS AND MINERALS	STRONG BONES, MAKING BLOOD	FRUITS, VEGETABLES

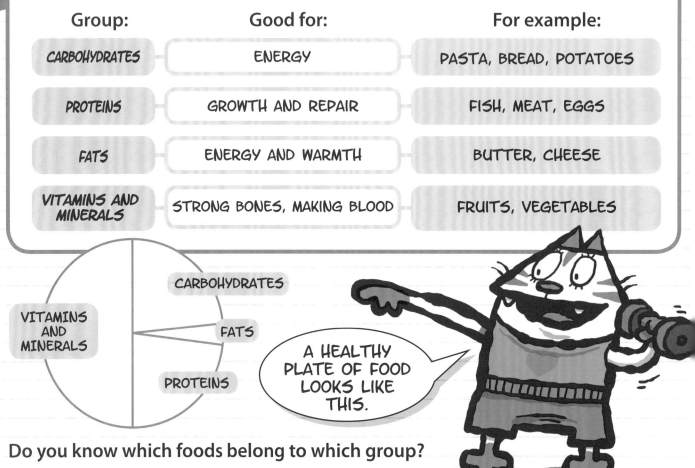

CARBOHYDRATES

VITAMINS AND MINERALS

FATS

PROTEINS

A HEALTHY PLATE OF FOOD LOOKS LIKE THIS.

Do you know which foods belong to which group?

Complete the sentences below. Use each word once.
You might want to put a cross through the word
once you've used it, so that you don't use it again.

a carrot

1. _____ is a source of fat.

chips

2. _____ is a source of protein.

an egg

3. _____ is a source of vitamins and minerals.

an apple

4. _____ are a source of carbohydrates.

butter

5. _____ is a source of protein.

salmon

6. _____ is a source of vitamins and minerals.

12

We need to eat more of some foods and less of other foods. Which foods do we need to eat more of? Which foods do we need to eat less of?

Complete the table below by sorting the foods from the following list:

salt	beefburgers	chocolate	salad
crisps	beans	whole grains	sweets
green vegetables	fruit	fatty foods	
chips	cakes	carrots	

Eat more	Eat less
	salt

NOW ADD MORE EXAMPLES OF YOUR OWN!

TEST IT OUT!

Remember, fluid is important too. About 70% of your body is water! You need to drink about 4 to 6 glasses of water per day to replace the fluids you lose as you sweat and go to the toilet.

Stick a reward sticker here!

13

Materials and magnets

Materials are what things are made of. Different materials have different properties. For example:

STEEL IS STRONG AND HARD. IT IS DIFFICULT TO BREAK.

PAPER IS SOFT AND WEAK. IT TEARS EASILY.

Complete the table below.

Material	Strong or weak?	Light or heavy?	Transparent or opaque?	Waterproof or not waterproof?
wood	STRONG			
steel				
polythene				
glass				
marble				

Draw a line to choose the most suitable material for each product and write why you paired them.

saucepans	wool	_____
gloves	pottery	_____
paving slabs	aluminium	_____
dinner plates	rubber	_____
bicycle tyres	metal	_____
kitchen foil	paper	_____
windows	stone	_____
books	fabric	_____
curtains	glass	_____

Conductor or insulator?

Heat travels easily through metal, pottery and glass. These materials are called conductors.

Heat does not travel easily through polystyrene, fabric, wood and plastic. These materials are called insulators.

Choose a good material to make the following products. Write the name of a suitable material next to each product.

An oven glove _____   A baking tray _____

A saucepan handle _____   A radiator _____

A container for a hot drink _____   A table mat _____

TEST IT OUT!

Use a magnet to find out which materials are attracted to magnets. Tick those materials that are magnetic in the list below.

COPPER ☐   IRON ☐   PLASTIC ☐

STEEL ☐   SILVER ☐   ALUMINIUM ☐

Magnets have many uses. Fill in the missing words. Choose from the following:

CREDIT   STEEL   ELECTRO   COMPASSES

1. Magnets are used to sort aluminium cans from _____ cans at recycling plants.

2. Magnetic strips contain information on _____ cards.

3. Magnets are used in _____ to tell us where magnetic North is.

4. _____-magnets are used to pick up or sort metal objects in manufacturing industries.

Do you know of any other uses for magnets? Write them here.

_____

_____

Stick a reward sticker here!

15

Solids, liquids and gases

All things in the universe are either: a solid, a liquid or a gas.

Draw a line to sort each of these materials into the correct group:

1. running water

2. ice cube

3. steam from a kettle

4. bubbles in a fizzy drink

5. hard-boiled egg

6. egg shell

7. raw egg

8. snow

SOLID

LIQUID

GAS

Get it?
Water can exist in all three states: as a solid, a liquid or a gas.

What happens to these things when they are heated? Write a sentence to describe how they change.

ice lolly _____

raw egg _____

water _____

What happens to these things when they are burned? Write a sentence to describe how they change.

bread _____

wood _____

candle _____

What happens to these things when they are frozen?
Write a sentence to describe how they change.

bread _____

tomato _____

orange juice _____

Sometimes we can reverse a change and get back what we started with.

For example: we can freeze water to get ice, then we can melt the ice to get water again. This is a reversible change. However, some changes are irreversible, which means we can't get back what we started with.

Are these changes reversible or irreversible? Draw a line to the correct word.

toast – Can we get the bread back?

ash – Can we get the wood back?

REVERSIBLE

fried egg – Can we get the raw egg back?

melted chocolate – Can we get solid chocolate back?

IRREVERSIBLE

frozen orange juice – Can we get the orange drink back?

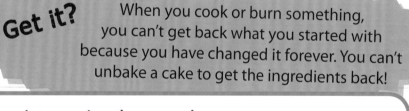

Get it? When you cook or burn something, you can't get back what you started with because you have changed it forever. You can't unbake a cake to get the ingredients back!

Read about the water cycle:

The wind and heat from the Sun cause water in seas, rivers and lakes to evaporate into a gas. As this gas rises, it cools (condenses) to form clouds, which are made up of tiny droplets of water. When the clouds rise over higher ground they cool further to form bigger droplets that fall as rain or snow.

Label the picture using these words:
evaporation, condensation, rain, snow.

17

Dissolving and separating

Stick a reward sticker here!

Some solids will dissolve in a liquid, e.g. instant drinking chocolate or instant coffee will dissolve in warm water. We say that these solids are 'soluble'.

TEST IT OUT!

Find out if these solids are soluble in tepid water:

A TEASPOON OF SALT ☐

A TEASPOON OF GRANULATED SUGAR ☐

A TEASPOON OF FLOUR ☐

A TEASPOON OF RICE ☐

A TEASPOON OF SAND ☐

A TEASPOON OF SOIL ☐

Carry out a 'fair test' and control any variables, e.g. make sure you use the same amount of water at the same temperature. Does the temperature of the water make any difference? Repeat the experiment using warmer water. What do you notice?

Record your results in this table:

Type of solid	Dissolves in water: Yes/No	Time taken to dissolve (measured in seconds)
salt		
sugar		
flour		
rice		
sand		
soil		

Get it?

When a solid dissolves in water, it makes a 'solution'. This means the solid has dissolved into the liquid so that the solid is no longer visible.

Solids that do not dissolve in water are called 'insoluble'.

18

How can we get solids back from mixtures?

Choose your equipment (from the examples below) and explain how you would use it to separate the following mixtures:

BUNSEN BURNER   SIEVE

MAGNET   FILTER PAPER

Get it?

When you come out of the sea on a hot day, the water quickly evaporates leaving the salt on your skin (or fur)!

1. To separate a solution of salt and water?

_____

_____

_____

_____

2. To separate a mixture of sand and water?

_____

_____

3. To separate out stones from soil?

_____

_____

4. To separate out paperclips from flour?

_____

_____

Stick a reward sticker here!

19

Can you hear it?

Sounds are made when an object vibrates.

WHEN YOU HIT A DRUM, THE DRUM SKIN VIBRATES.

WHEN YOU PLAY A GUITAR, THE STRINGS VIBRATE.

Sounds travel in waves. We can hear the sound of the guitar when air molecules around the guitar vibrate and send sound waves to reach our ears.

This is what the inside of the human ear looks like.

OUTER EAR

TINY BONES

NERVES

EARDRUM

EAR CANAL

SEMICIRCULAR CANALS

COCHLEA

Choose from these words to complete the description of how the human ear works. The labelled diagram above will help you.

COCHLEA　　STIRRUP　　BRAIN　　NERVES　　SOUNDS　　EARDRUM

The _____ vibrates when _____ enter the ear and three tiny

bones called the hammer, anvil and _____ amplify the sound. Once inside

the inner ear, the sound passes to the _____. Here the sound is changed

into electrical signals that travel along _____ to the _____.

KEEP THE NOISE DOWN!

Sound can travel through solids such as walls and glass. We know this because, when we are inside a building, we can hear sound coming from outside.

HOWL!

Sounds can travel through water – whale song can travel over 2,000 kilometres underwater.

Which is it: loud or quiet?
Write 'loud' or 'quiet' to complete the statements below.

A _____ sound makes a large sound wave.

A _____ sound makes a small sound wave.

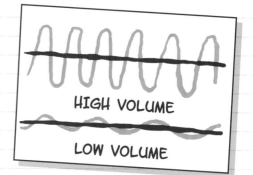

HIGH VOLUME

LOW VOLUME

The sound of music!

Each note we play on a musical instrument has a pitch (or frequency).

High-pitched notes (made by faster vibrations) have a high frequency and a short wavelength.
Low-pitched notes (made by slower vibrations) have a low frequency and a long wavelength.

Which is it: lower or higher?
Write 'lower' or 'higher' to complete the statements below.

A longer sound wave has a _____ pitch.

A shorter sound wave has a _____ pitch.

TEST IT OUT!

Make a glass xylophone:

Pour different amounts of water into three glasses (be sure to ask a grown-up which glasses you can use!). Gently tap the rim of the glass with a spoon. Which glass makes the highest pitch? Which makes the lowest pitch?

Stick a reward sticker here!

21

Can you see it?

Light travels from a source such as the Sun, a candle flame, a fire or an electric light bulb. We see objects when light from a source reflects off those objects into our eyes. That's why we can't see in the dark.

Join the names for the parts of the eye to the descriptions below.

1. Light enters the eye through this.

2. Light is focussed in this part of the eye.

3. This converts light into electrical nerve signals.

4. Nerve signals travel along this part to the brain.

retina

pupil

optic nerve

lens

Cats and dogs have better night vision than humans because they have a reflective layer behind the retina that reflects light back into the eye.

TEST IT OUT!

Next time you are travelling in a car at night, look out for road markings called 'Cat's Eyes'. They are usually in the middle of the road. They are made of a reflective material to reflect back the light from the cars' headlights into our eyes.

22

Complete the statements below. Choose from the following words:

SHINY   SHADOW   REFRACTED   STRAIGHT

TRANSPARENT   REFLECTION   OPAQUE

1. Light travels in a _____ line.

2. When light is blocked by an _____ object a _____ is formed, which is a similar shape to the object.

3. When light hits a _____ surface, such as a mirror, a _____ occurs.

4. When light hits a _____ surface, such as water, it is _____ into a rainbow of colours.

Mirror, mirror!

Read the description of a periscope below, then draw a diagram of a periscope in the space provided below.

Inside a periscope there are two mirrors connected by a tube. The light reflects off the first mirror and then off the second mirror so a person looking through the tubes can see over the top of objects.

Get it?

Raindrops in a rainbow act like prisms to split sunlight into a spectrum of colours.

Stick a reward sticker here!

23

Gravity and other forces

Forces push and pull objects.

Gravity is a force that pulls all objects towards each other. On Earth, gravity pulls objects downwards to the ground. That's why, no matter how hard or how high you throw a ball, it will always fall back to the ground.

BUT YOU CAN SLOW THE RATE OF FALL OF AN OBJECT BY INCREASING ITS SURFACE AREA, E.G. BY ADDING A PARACHUTE!

TEST IT OUT!

Take two sheets of A4 paper. Scrunch one sheet into a ball but leave the other sheet flat. Now throw both into air at the same time. Which falls faster? Why?

Get it?

A bird flies when the upward force (or the 'lift') from its wings is greater than the force of gravity pulling it down!

We can measure the force of gravity using a force meter. We call this force 'weight'. Force is measured in Newtons (N).

What does the ball weigh in Newtons?
Read the scale on the force meter.

The ball weighs _____ N (equal to 300 grams).

'Newtons' are named after Sir Isaac Newton, a famous scientist and mathematician who discovered that gravity acts on all objects in the Universe.

24

The pull of gravity on the Moon is smaller than on Earth. Because of this, everything on the Moon weighs less! Objects are weightless in the absence of gravity.

Complete the statements below. Choose from the following words:

FRICTION   AIR RESISTANCE   WATER RESISTANCE   UPTHRUST

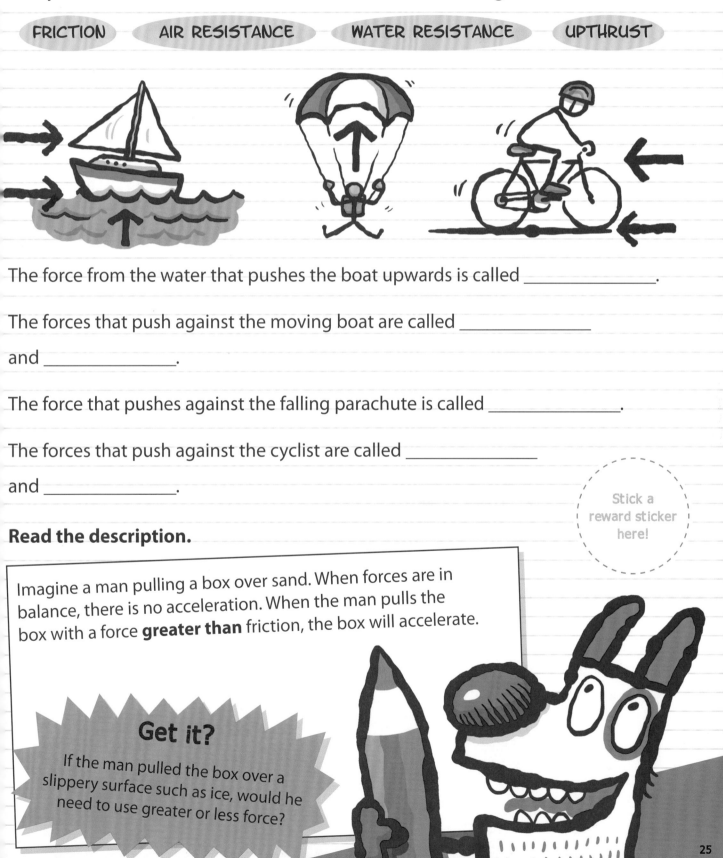

The force from the water that pushes the boat upwards is called _____.

The forces that push against the moving boat are called _____

and _____.

The force that pushes against the falling parachute is called _____.

The forces that push against the cyclist are called _____

and _____.

Read the description.

Imagine a man pulling a box over sand. When forces are in balance, there is no acceleration. When the man pulls the box with a force **greater than** friction, the box will accelerate.

Stick a reward sticker here!

Get it?

If the man pulled the box over a slippery surface such as ice, would he need to use greater or less force?

25

Electricity

Many appliances found in our homes, e.g. refrigerators, cookers, TVs, computers, lights, heaters, etc., are powered by electricity. Electricity comes from the mains supply (travelling through wires in the walls) or from batteries that power smaller devices such as mobile phones and torches.

Electricity is extremely useful. It can provide us with light, heat, movement and sound. Look around your home for examples of electrical devices and complete the table below.

Type of appliance	It provides us with...
KETTLE	HOT WATER

ELECTRICITY FROM THE MAINS IS POWERFUL AND DANGEROUS. 240 VOLTS OF ELECTRICITY CAN TRAVEL THROUGH A WALL SOCKET — THAT'S ENOUGH TO KILL SOMEONE!

Danger zone!

Get it?

Stay safe around electricity. Remember these never-evers:

• NEVER EVER USE ELECTRICAL APPLIANCES NEAR WATER.

• NEVER EVER TOUCH WALL SOCKETS OR SWITCHES WITH WET HANDS.

• NEVER EVER POKE YOUR FINGER INTO A WALL SOCKET.

Electrical circuits have components. Learn the symbols for the following components.

wire	battery	bulb	open switch	closed switch	buzzer	motor

In an electrical circuit, electricity flows from one end of the battery through the wires and components back to the other end of the battery. However, if there is a break in the circuit, electricity will not flow.

Which of the below circuits are working properly and which are not?
Put a tick or a cross next to each one.

A.   **B.**   **C.**   **D.**

Explain why you think those circuits you marked with a cross are not working.

_____

_____

This circuit shows a battery, a bulb and a switch.

What will happen to the brightness of the bulb if…

1. another battery is added to the circuit?

_____

2. another bulb is added to the circuit?

_____

Stick a reward sticker here!

27

Sun, Earth and Moon

Fill in the missing numbers and words in the facts below.

Choose from the following: *24, 28, 365, Earth, Sun*

It takes _____ days for the Earth to orbit the _____ .

It takes _____ hours for the _____ to rotate once on its axis.

It takes the Moon _____ days to orbit the Earth.

Label the Earth and the Moon in the diagram below.

The Sun's gravitational pull keeps the Earth in orbit. The Earth's gravitational pull keeps the Moon in orbit.

TEST IT OUT!

Attach string to a ball and swing it around your head. If you imagine you are the Sun and the ball is the Earth then the string acts like the pull of the Sun's gravity.

Day and night

The Earth rotates on an axis and this gives us day and night. From the diagram below, you can see that on the part of the Earth facing the Sun it is daytime but on the part of the Earth turning away from the Sun it is night-time.

Label 'day' and 'night' on this diagram.

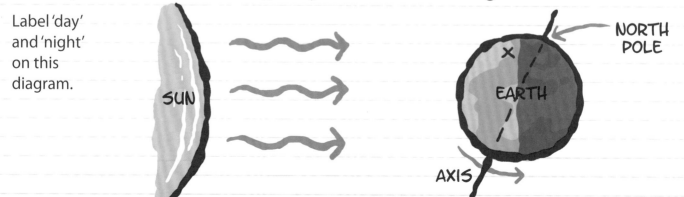

When we look at the Moon from Earth it seems to change shape – sometimes we see a thin crescent shape and at other times we see a full circle. However, the Moon doesn't really change shape, it only appears that way because we are looking at the Moon as it reflects light from the Sun.

If you imagine you are standing on the Earth in the diagram below, you can see that the Moon would look different in each phase.

AWOO!

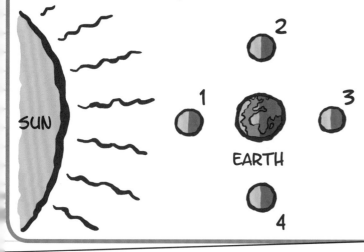

SUN

EARTH

1. New Moon (1 day/28 days)
2. Half Moon (7 days)
3. Full Moon (14 days)
4. Half Moon (21 days)

Look outside your window tonight. Draw the Moon as you see it in the space below. Compare your drawing to the diagram above. In which phase is the Moon in your drawing?

Stick a reward sticker here!

29

Sun and shadows

If you look south at different times of the day, the Sun seems to move across the sky from east to west.

In the early morning, the Sun is low in the sky and this creates long shadows. At midday, the Sun is at its highest and shadows are shortest. Then in the evening, as the Sun goes down, shadows lengthen once more.

You might think that the Sun is moving, but in reality the Sun is staying still and it is the Earth that is turning.

TEST IT OUT!

Wait for a sunny day. Place a wooden spoon or stick in the ground, facing south. Mark the shadow of the stick on the ground using a length of string. After an hour, check the shadow. What do you notice? Mark the position of the new shadow with another piece of string. If you do this at hourly intervals you can make a shadow clock!

Match each shadow to the correct time of day.

MORNING   EVENING   MIDDAY

Stick a reward sticker here!

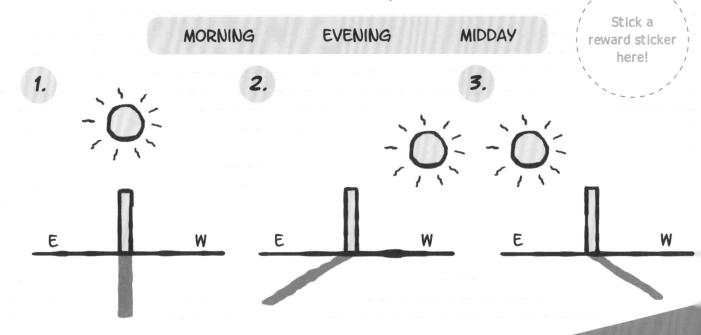

Answers

Pages 2-3

acorn seedling: **alive**
fallen autumn leaf: **was once alive**
plank of wood: **was once alive**
pebble: **never alive**
brick: **never alive**
hopping rabbit: **alive**

1. The flowers attract insect pollinators. The male parts of the flower produce **pollen**. When the flowers die, fruits and **seeds** are formed.
2. The **leaves** use sunlight to turn carbon dioxide and water into **food** – a process called photosynthesis.
3. The **stem** carries nutrients and water from the roots to the leaves and **flowers**. It also holds the plant upright so that it can grow towards the Sun.
4. The **roots** hold the plant in the ground and soak up water and nutrients from the **soil**.

1. pollen	3. ovary	5. stigma	7. seeds
2. stamen	4. pollinator	6. petal	8. sepal

Pages 4-5

Seeds are scattered by the wind and animals	**4**
Plants are pollinated by insects and the wind	**2**
Seeds germinate and new plants start to grow	**1**
Fertilised plants make fruits and seeds	**3**

Seed dispersal – A: 1, B: 3, C: 2, D: 5, E: 4

Page 6-7

grass > **slug** > thrush
grass > **rabbit** > fox
grass > insect > **frog** > hawk

Possible answers:

Crocodile – long, powerful tail for swimming; sharp teeth for snatching prey; nostrils positioned above the water for breathing while resting.

Owl – large, forward-facing eyes for binocular vision; head can rotate to see all around; curved claws for gripping branches and prey; powerful wings for flight.

Tiger – striped coat for camouflage amongst trees; sharp, pointed teeth and powerful jaws for catching prey; powerful legs and body for running.

long, sharply-pointed beak – **heron**
large, trumpet-shaped ears – **impala**
sharp spines on body – **hedgehog**
skin that matches its surroundings – **leaf frog**
thick layer of body fat – **seal**
long snout and tongue – **anteater**

Pages 8-9

Does it have 6 legs? **Yes – housefly**
Does it have 8 legs? **Yes – spider**
Does it have more than 20 legs? **Yes – millipede**
Does it have a shell? **Yes – snail**
Does it have a shell? **No – slug**

Definition	Belongs to the group called:	Example
Breeds in water but spends time on land	AMPHIBIAN	FROG
Cold blooded, breathes air and has scales	REPTILE	CROCODILE
Cold blooded, has scales and gills, lives in water	FISH	SALMON
Warm blooded, young feed on milk	MAMMAL	APE
Has feathers and wings	BIRD	DUCK

1. frogspawn 2. tadpole 3. froglet 4. frog
1. egg 2. caterpillar 3. pupa 4. butterfly
1. egg 2. larva 3. cocoon 4. ant
1. egg 2. baby 3. child 4. teenager 5. adult

Differences between the human life cycle and a housefly's life cycle – possible answers: the human life cycle has more stages than the housefly cycle. The housefly cycle has a 'maggot' stage before the 'adult' stage, but the human cycle has a 'child' and 'teenager' stage before the 'adult' stage.

Pages 10-11

heart – pumps blood around the body
lungs – pass oxygen into the blood
stomach – processes and digests food
brain – controls all the activities in the body
nerves – carry messages from the brain

These things are bad for your heart: *fatty foods, tobacco, lack of exercise, alcohol, drugs, lots of salt.*

Your **heart** works like a pump. It has two sides so that blood can go in two directions: one artery pumps **blood** to the lungs and the other artery pumps blood to the rest of the body.

Your blood contains **oxygen** and food which your body needs. When you exercise, your **body** uses more oxygen so your heart beats faster to increase the supply.

Your lungs are like sponges filled with tiny pockets of air. When you breathe in you are filling your **lungs** with oxygen and when you breathe out you are breathing out **carbon dioxide**.

liver – cleans your blood and stores vitamins
kidneys – filter waste from your blood and make urine
bladder – stores urine
skeleton – protects your organs and helps you to move
blood vessels – carry food and oxygen to the body cells

Pages 12-13

1. **butter** is a source of fat. 2. **an egg** is a source of protein. 3. **a carrot** is a source of vitamins and minerals. 4. **chips** are a source of carbohydrates. 5. **salmon** is a source of protein. 6. **an apple** is a source of vitamins and minerals.

Eat more	Eat less	
green vegetables	**salt**	**sweets**
fruit	**crisps**	
whole grains	**beefburgers**	
beans	**cakes**	
carrots	**chocolate**	
salad	**fatty foods**	
	chips	

Pages 14-15

Material	Strong or weak?	Light or heavy?	Transparent or opaque?	Waterproof or not waterproof?
wood	STRONG	EITHER	OPAQUE	EITHER
steel	STRONG	HEAVY	OPAQUE	WATERPROOF
polythene	STRONG	LIGHT	EITHER	WATERPROOF
glass	STRONG	HEAVY	TRANSPARENT	WATERPROOF
marble	STRONG	HEAVY	OPAQUE	WATERPROOF

Please note: your table may have some alternative answers depending on the type and thickness of the material.

saucepans – **metal**
gloves – **wool**
paving slabs– **stone**
dinner plates – **pottery**
bicycle tyres – **rubber**

kitchen foil – **aluminium**
windows – **glass**
books – **paper**
curtains – **fabric**

An oven glove - **fabric**
A saucepan handle – **wood or plastic**
A container for a hot drink – **pottery or polystyrene**
A baking tray – **metal**
A radiator – **metal**
A table mat – **wood or plastic**

COPPER ✗   IRON ✓   PLASTIC ✗
STEEL ✓   SILVER ✗   ALUMINIUM ✗

1. Magnets are used to sort aluminium cans from **steel** cans
   at recycling plants.
2. Magnetic strips contain information on **credit** cards.
3. Magnets are used in **compasses** to tell us where magnetic North is.
4. **Electro**-magnets are used to pick up or sort metal objects
   in manufacturing industries.

Other uses: fridge magnets, magnetic door seals, magnetic toys, etc.

Pages 16-17

1. running water – liquid
2. ice cube – solid
3. steam from a kettle – gas
4. bubbles in a fizzy drink – gas
5. hard-boiled egg – solid
6. egg shell – solid
7. raw egg – liquid
8. snow – solid

The ice lolly melts and changes from a solid to a liquid.
The raw egg cooks and changes from a liquid to a solid.
The water boils and some of the water changes from a liquid to a gas.

Bread: Goes brown, hardens and changes to toast.
Wood: Changes to ash. Smoke from the flames produces a gas
(carbon dioxide).
Candle: The flame burns and melts the wax. Smoke from the flames
produces a gas (carbon dioxide).

Bread: goes hard; water contained in the bread solidifies.
Tomato: goes hard; water contained in the tomato crystallises into
a solid.
Orange juice: freezes and changes from a liquid to a solid.

toast – irreversible – we can't get the uncooked bread back
ash – irreversible – we can't get the wood back
fried egg – irreversible – we can't get the raw egg back
melted chocolate – reversible – cool the chocolate to make it
solid again
frozen juice – reversible – heat the frozen juice to make it liquid again

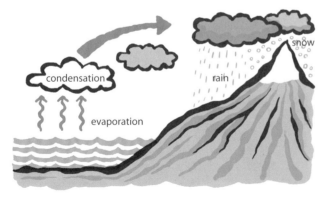

Pages 18-19

1. To separate a solution of salt and water: *If we warm a solution of salt
and water using a Bunsen burner, the water will evaporate and leave the
salt behind.*

2. To separate a mixture of sand and water: *If we pour the sand and
water through filter paper the water will pass through the paper and the
sand will be left behind.*

3. To separate out stones from soil: *If we tip the soil and stones into a
sieve the smaller particles of soil will pass through the holes in the sieve
but the stones will be too large to pass through and they will be left behind.*

4. To separate out paperclips from flour: *If we use a magnet the
paperclips will be attracted to the magnet and will stick to it but the
flour will not.*

Pages 20-21

The **eardrum** vibrates when **sounds** enter the ear and three tiny bones
called the hammer, anvil and **stirrup** amplify the sound. Once inside
the inner ear, the sound passes to the **cochlea**. Here the sound is
changed into electrical signals that travel along **nerves** to the **brain**.

A loud sound makes a large sound wave.
A quiet sound makes a small sound wave.

A longer sound wave has a lower pitch.
A shorter sound wave has a higher pitch.

Pages 22-23

1. pupil
2. lens
3. retina
4. optic nerve

1. Light travels in a **straight** line.
2. When light is blocked by an **opaque** object a **shadow** is formed.
3. When light hits a **shiny** surface such as a mirror a **reflection** occurs.
4. When light hits a **transparent** surface such as water it is **refracted**
   into a rainbow of colours.

Pages 24-25

Test it out! The scrunched up paper fell faster because it had less air
resistance acting on it. The flat sheet of paper fell at a slower rate
because its shape created more air resistance.

The ball weighs 3 N.

The force from the water that pushes the boat upwards is
called **upthrust**.
The forces that push against the moving boat are called **water
resistance** and **air resistance**.
The force that pushes against the falling parachute is called **air
resistance**.
The forces that push against the cyclist are called **air resistance**
and **friction**.
**When the man pulls the box with a force greater than friction,
the box moves.** He would use less force to pull the box over a
slippery surface.

Pages 26-27

A. ✗ Electricity will not flow because the switch is open.
B. ✓ This circuit is working.
C. ✗ Electricity will not flow because there is a break in the wire.
D. ✗ Electricity will not flow because the battery is not connected
   at one end.
1. If you add another battery the flow of electricity in the circuit
   will increase and the light from the bulb will be brighter.
2. If you add another bulb the flow of electricity in the circuit
   will decrease and the light from both bulbs will be dimmer.

Pages 28-29

It takes **365** days for the Earth to orbit the **Sun**.
It takes **24** hours for the **Earth** to rotate once on its axis.
It takes the Moon **28** days to orbit the Earth.

Page 30

1. midday
2. evening
3. morning